MAXIMUM RIDE

WHAT CAME BEFORE

Max and her flock are genetic experiments. Created by a mysterious lab known only as the "School," their genetic codes have been spliced with avian DNA, giving them wings and the power to soar. What they lack are homes, families, and memories of a real life.

After escaping from the School, the flock is hunted by Erasers, agents of the School who can transform into terrifying wolf creatures, and Jeb Batchelder, the man they once thought of as a father. Despite the targets on their backs, the flock is desperate to learn about their individual pasts, and their inquiries lead them to Washington, D.C., where they meet Special Agent Anne Walker of the FBI, who takes them in and gives the flock a taste of a normal life — only to betray them in the end.

On their own again, the flock heads to Florida, following a lead on a multi-national corporation called ITEX that seems to have been pulling the flock's strings all along. Once there, Max is kidnapped by ITEX and replaced by a clone of herself — Max 2.0! With a bit of unexpected help from Jeb, Max escapes ITEX and rescues the flock from her doppelgänger.

Heading west, the kids find that ITEX has gone troublingly quiet and decide that a very public appearance is in order to try to draw them out. Unfortunately for the flock, their plan is a bit too successful, as they have their first encounter with the company's new and improved mechanical Erasers. Where it all goes truly wrong, however, is when one of their own switches sides… Who would have expected Angel to turn on the others in an effort to secure her survival in the world that remains after ITEX reduces the world's population by half?

As Max and the flock await extermination, will Angel turn out to be their executioner…or their salvation?

CHARACTER INTRODUCTION

MAXIMUM RIDE

Max is the eldest member of the flock, and the responsibility of caring for her comrades has fallen to her. Tough and uncompromising, she's willing to put everything on the line to protect her "family."

FANG

Only slightly younger than Max, Fang is one of the elder members of the flock. Cool and reliable, Fang is Max's rock. He may be the strongest of them all, but most of the time it is hard to figure out what is on his mind.

IGGY

Being blind doesn't mean that Iggy is helpless. He has not only an incredible sense of hearing, but also a particular knack (and fondness) for explosives.

NUDGE

Motormouth Nudge would probably spend most days at the mall if not for her pesky mutant-bird-girl-being-hunted-by-wolf-men problem.

GASMAN

The name pretty much says it all. The Gasman (or Gazzy) has the art of flatulence down to a science. He's also Angel's biological big brother.

ANGEL

The youngest member of the flock and Gazzy's little sister, Angel seems to have some peculiar abilities — mind reading, for example.

ARI

Just seven years old, Ari is Jeb's son but was transformed into an Eraser. He appears to have a particular axe to grind with Max.

JEB BATCHELDER

The flock's former benefactor, Jeb was a scientist at the School before helping the flock to make their original escape.

WHAM!

DON'T LET THEM GET AWAY!!

BLAM

BLAM

BLAM

BLAM

MAX!

ANGEL, GOOD JOB!

......

MAX, YOU ARE WAY OUT OF LINE. THERE'S NO WAY HE'S COMING WITH US!

GRAB!

HE SAVED OUR LIVES.

THEY'RE GOING TO KILL HIM.

HE'S TRIED TO KILL US A HUNDRED TIMES!

MAX, ARI'S REALLY MEAN. HE'S TRIED TO HURT YOU.

I DON'T WANT HIM WITH US!

ME NEITHER! HE'S ONE OF THEM!

I THINK HE'S CHANGED.

HE HELPED GET US OUT.

AND HE FOUND TOTAL FOR US.

OH NO, OH NO.

KA-BOOM

AND A-THR—

AND A-ONE...

AND A-TWO...

WAY TO BE!

YEAH. WAY TO BE LOUD AND OBVIOUS ABOUT WHERE WE ARE.

BOOM!!

AIEE!

!!

BIG GARAGE FULL OF BIG CARS WITH BIG GAS TANKS.

THAT FELT GREAT.

......

MAX?

YES?

I'M HUNGRY. WE ALREADY WENT THROUGH EVERYTHING WE HAD IN THE PACKS.

Argh. I don't want to be near him!

I THINK THE OTHERS ARE HUNGRY TOO. TOTAL KEEPS WHINING — YOU KNOW WHAT HE'S LIKE.

......

UH-HUH.

SO, UH, IS THERE A PLAN TO STOP SOME-WHERE? GET SOME FOOD?

THERE'S ALWAYS A PLAN.

REMEMBER THE SKI HOUSE WE FOUND IN COLORADO?

MAYBE IT'S STILL UNOCCUPIED. BE A PLACE TO REST UP.

WHERE ARE YOU GOING? A LITTLE HIDEAWAY THAT ARI KNOWS ABOUT?

NO WAY! YOU KNOW THE RULES— NEVER RETURN TO A PLACE YOU'VE BEEN!

IF SOMEONE'S BEEN THERE, THEY WOULD HAVE BEEFED UP THEIR SECURITY.

IF NO ONE'S BEEN THERE, WE PRETTY MUCH CLEANED OUT ALL THE FOOD ANYWAY!

I'VE THOUGHT OF THAT.

BUT WE NEED SOME DOWNTIME, AND IT'S OUR BEST OPTION.

IT IS NOT! WE SHOULD FIND A CANYON OR CAVE SOMEWHERE AND HUNKER DOWN—

OKAY, DID YOU LOCK UP?

YEAH. AND THE FIRE'S OUT.

GOOD. I CAN'T WAIT TO COME BACK.

MAYBE SATURDAY, RIGHT?

VROOM—

YOU KNOW WHAT DAY TODAY IS?

...TUES-DAY.

GRIN

TSK.

CLICK

CREAK...

IT'S WARM!

FOOD! BEEF STEW, BUTTER, APPLES!

THEY EVEN HAVE SOME DOG FOOD!

YOU'RE KIDDING ME, RIGHT?

ARI, CAN YOU EAT THIS?

......

GRAB!

COME HERE FOR A SECOND.

ME OR HIM.

CHOOSE NOW.

....

GOSH, FANG, YOU ROMANTIC FOOL, HOW INCREDIBLY SEXIST-PIG OF YOU.

HA!

NOT AS A BOYFRIEND, YOU IDIOT! I MEANT AS A MEMBER OF THIS FLOCK!

I'M NOT GOING TO STAY WHILE YOU LET SOMEONE WHO'S TRIED TO KILL BOTH OF US, MORE THAN ONCE, STAY!

EITHER HE GOES OR I GO!

...IF I THINK ABOUT IT, I'LL FIGURE THAT SENTENCE OUT.

BUT I DON'T HAVE TO CHOOSE BETWEEN YOU! PEOPLE CHANGE!

HE HELPED SAVE OUR LIVES. HE WORKED WITH ANGEL. AND WHILE WE WERE THERE, HE LET ME IN ON SOME OF THE STUFF GOING ON AT THE SCHOOL!

YEAH, AND I'M SURE HE HAD NO ULTERIOR MOTIVE FOR THAT! I'M SURE HE'S NOT WIRED, NOT TRACKING US, NOT TELLING EVERYONE WHERE WE ARE RIGHT THIS SECOND!

I'M SURE ALL THE BRAIN-WASHING AND TRAINING JUST WORE OFF ONCE YOU BATTED YOUR EYES AT HIM!

HE'S SEVEN YEARS OLD, YOU JERK!

AND I'M NOT BATTING MY EYES AT ANYONE. NOT YOU, NOT HIM, NOT ANYONE! HE DOESN'T EVEN THINK LIKE THAT.

HE'S TOXIC! THEY'VE POLLUTED HIM AND SCREWED HIM UP SO MUCH HE CAN'T EVEN THINK.

ARI'S A KILLER!

......

HE'S A TOTAL LIABILITY, AND YOU'RE OUT OF YOUR MIND IF YOU THINK IT'S FINE THAT HE'S HERE!

OKAY. I REALLY THINK HE'S CHANGED...

...AND HIS EXPIRATION DATE IS GONNA KICK IN SOON, ANYWAY.

BUT I KNOW HIS BEING HERE IS BUMMING EVERYONE OUT.

YOU PICKED UP ON THAT, HUH, SHERLOCK?

I'M TRYING TO MEET YOU HALFWAY, NIMROD! I WAS GOING TO SAY LET ME THINK ABOUT IT.

I'LL KEEP AN EAGLE EYE ON HIM. FIRST SIGN OF ANYTHING SUSPICIOUS, I'LL KICK HIS BUTT OUT MYSELF. OKAY?

ARE YOU NUTS? ARI NEEDS TO GO NOW!

THE REST OF YOU GET SOME SLEEP.

......

CLICK

THANKS.

Fang's Blog

TO EVERYONE, EVERYWHERE
WARNING
HEADS-UP
EVIL SCIENTISTS WILL END LIFE AS WE KNOW IT

Fang
Today's date:
**Already Too
Late!**

Visitor number
28,772,461

And even as we don't know it.
I know what it's called now, folks. It's called the Re-
Evolution Plan. And the By-Half Plan. We got out of the
School (anyone who wants to bomb them, feel free).
Now we're in hiding, ha-ha. While we were there, we
found out that the plan is to basically KILL anyone
with any kind of disease or weakness. The only people
left will be perfectly healthy and have useful skills. So
everyone bone up on something useful! Or go into
hiding. And if you have the sniffles, crawl under a rock
and don't come out.

What would be useful, you ask? I've made a chart.

USEFUL	NOT USEFUL
Plumber	Politician
Carpenter	Publicist
Boat builder	Art history buff
Farmer	Celebrity chef
Sanitation crew	Interior designer
Cattle rancher	Pet psychic
Scientist	Celebrity rock/pop/hip-hop star
Military	Teen idol
Medical personnel	Life coach

So this would be a good time to examine your career
goals.
Last time I checked, more than 28 million people had
hit this blog. Way to go, people. Save yourselves. Save
your brothers and sisters. Don't let the whitecoats get
you.

And if you see any flying kids, keep your mouth shut.

— Fang, from somewhere in America

Comment Wall (1,805 comments) ▼

TAP...

......

...HMM.

TWENTY-EIGHT MILLION PEOPLE HAVE CLICKED ON THE BLOG.

HUH.

Good lord.

YOU'RE BASING YOUR PLAN FOR HUMAN SALVATION ON A VOICE INSIDE YOUR HEAD.

PACK PACK

A VOICE THAT ISN'T ACTUALLY JUST YOU TALKING TO YOURSELF. RIGHT?

ARE YOU OUT OF YOUR MIND?!

I'M BASING MINE ON THE INFORMATION FROM MY BLOG.

I'VE DECIDED TO GO MY OWN WAY.

MAX...

ALMOST ANYONE'S WELCOME TO COME WITH ME.

SWISH

GLARESS

I THINK WE SHOULD ALL STICK TOGETHER UNTIL FANG COMES BACK!

YOU GUYS SHOULDN'T DO THIS.

YOU CRAZY KIDS.

WE HAVE TO CHOOSE?

I'LL GO WITH FANG.

IGGY!

SSK...

NO-BRAINER.

MAX.

FINE.

FINE!

....

ENGLAND, FIRST. START WITH ENGLAND.

LOOK FOR SCHOOLS.

ENGLAND.

WE'RE GOING TO LOOK FOR SCHOOLS.

LEARN EVERYTHING WE CAN ABOUT THIS RE-EVOLUTION PLAN.

AND WE'RE GOING TO HAVE TO MOVE FAST.

MAX.

I'M ON YOUR SIDE.

I'M GOING TO PROTECT YOU NO MATTER WHAT.

UNTIL MY EXPIRATION DATE, ANYWAY.

OKAY, THEN.

WE HEAD EAST!

MAXIMUM
RIDE

MAXIMUM
RIDE
CHAPTER 36

L.A., VENICE BEACH

I HATE YOU! YOU'RE SUCH LOSERS!

YOU'RE JUST BEING JERKS.

KICK

OWW!

WHAT'S WRONG WITH YOU?

DESCRIBE. THE. PEOPLE.

THERE'S A MILLION PEOPLE.

THIS IS VENICE BEACH, HOME OF ROLLER DISCO. I SMELL COCONUT OIL. I HEAR HIGH-PITCHED GIGGLES.

I KNOW WE MUST BE SURROUNDED BY BEACH BUNNIES...

...AND YOU'RE LOOKING AT A MAP!

......

WHAT'S A BEACH BUNNY?

BEACH BUNNY, SCHMEACH BUNNY. WHO CARES?

AS LONG AS THEY'RE NOT FLYBOYS.

You can see them. I can't. Just do me a favor!

...Okay, fine.

SIGH...

THERE ARE TWO GIRLS OVER THERE.

ONE'S IN A WHITE BIKINI. ONE HAS "UTOPIA" WRITTEN ACROSS HER BUTT.

THEY HAVE BIG, BLOND HAIR.

LET'S SEE...

UM, OVER THERE IS AN ASIAN GIRL, SKATING ON ROLLERBLADES, WITH HER DOG...

...LIKE A GREYHOUND OR SOMETHING, RUNNING BESIDE HER.

OOPS, SHE ALMOST TOOK OUT THAT STROLLER.

WHAT'S SHE WEARING?

A STRIPED BIKINI.

AND KNEE GUARDS.

OH, MAN. MORE, MORE.

MAX WOULD HAVE BEEN ALL OVER HIM LIKE UGLY ON AN APE, TELLING HIM WHAT A SEXIST PIG HE WAS.

Sorry

Fang's Blog

Busted-up Hollywood

Fang
Today's date:
**Already Too
Late!**

So, for those of you in the LA area, I need to fess up about the major wreckage over at the big Hollywood sign. A million hopefuls have fixated on that sign as a symbol of future movie careers, and I sure do apologize about it being destroyed. But it wasn't my fault.
The Gasman, Iggy, and I were minding our own business somewhere in the greater LA area (which extends from Tijuana up to Pismo Beach), and suddenly, out of nowhere, a couple hundred Flyboys dropped down on us. How did they know where we were? I always assumed they tracked us either by Max's chip or by Angel's dog.
Which, as you've probably heard, are with us no longer.
So how'd they know where to find us?
Unless one of us three is telling them?
Which is impossible, of course. Anyway, like I told you before, Max saw thousands of Flyboys back at the School, hanging in rows, charging up. So today they let a bunch of 'em go for a test-drive.
I have to tell you people, those things are fast. They're strong. They can go for a long time without stopping. But smart? Not so much.
Gaz, Iggy, and I shot up, fast, from where we'd been innocently hanging out. We're always better off in the air. Of course jaws dropped, eyes popped, small children screamed, etc., when we suddenly whipped out wings and took flight. I guess we're unusual even for LA.
The three of us against a couple hundred Flyboys?
I don't think so. Sure, maybe sixty, or even eighty, no problem. But not two hundred. Not even if Max were there. Well, okay, maybe if Max were there. Maybe the two hundred. But she wasn't there.
Anyway, Gaz, Iggy, and I instinctively implemented a tried-and-true plan of action, Plan Delta, which we've used any number of times and have down to an art. Basically it means "run like hell." Or rather, "fly like hell."
We flew. We zipped out of there like lightning. The Flyboys don't seem to have altitude problems — they followed us easily up into 747 cruising altitude, where even I was getting a little short of breath. Like the Erasers, they're not too nimble, but they're wicked fast and scarily strong.
One of Iggy's newest explosives took out about fifty of them, and sorry to all those folks showered by bits of Flyboy metal and flesh matrix down at that MTV party on the beach. The rest of them tore after us, and we couldn't outrun them.
Then I saw the Hollywood Hills. We flew right for the sign and, at the very, very last second, screamed into a direct vertical climb. I mean, my belt buckle scraped one of the letters. But the three of us made it, shooting straight up like rockets.
The Flyboys were not so fortunate.
One after another, they plowed right into the sign, setting off electrical charges that shorted them out and made quite a few of them explode like metallic, furry popcorn. And if you think that's a gross description, be glad you weren't there, being pelted by the little pieces. I think only about six or seven of them managed to avoid the carnage, and I have no idea what happened to them.
After we'd busted our sides laughing, we blew out of there, and now we're hiding. Again.
Us: roughly 200. Hard to tell with all the parts flying.
Them: 0
Take that, you whitecoat schmucks. Now you owe California a new Hollywood sign.

— Fang, somewhere in the West

Visitor number
972,361,007

Comment Wall(108 comments) ▼

Fang's Blog

108 comments ▼

Fang
Today's date:
**Already Too
Late!**

Visitor number
972,361,007

Kewl dude 326 said . . .
O man Fang thats so awesome, i mean when u guys popped all the flyboys. i
would a been bustin my gut 2. Keep flyin, man.
San Diego 11:51 AM

Sugargrrl said . . .
Dear Fang, I'm so glad your alright. I hate those flyboys and hope they all crash
and burn. If u need a place to stay in Roanoke, Virginia, just e-mail me.
12:14 PM

Heather said . . .
We should all make posses and search everywhere for labs and Schools
and stuff! There are millions and millions of kids in the world, and we can fix
what the grown-ups have polluted and destroyed! Landfills and oil slicks and
endangered species and wiping out forests and driving gas hogs and not caring
about the environment and not caring about animals! Their time of destroying
everything is over! It's time for Green Kids to unite!
Heather Schmidt
President, GreenKidsforaGreenerPlanet.org
12:57 PM

Streetfightr said . . .
Us kidz got 2 take over! De groneups hav recked everything! Dere destroyin r
whole planet! De kidz shuld run everything! Dey want us 2 b quiet! We won't b
quiet no more!
Brooklyn 1:20 PM

Chen Wei said . . .
Fang, I was wondering: do u have a girlfriend? Hong Kong
P.S. I am 15 years old but look younger.
2:40 PM

Carlos said . . .
I say we burn all the science labs! Make all the grown-ups into slaves!
Texas 3:07 PM

Anonymous said . . .
Carlos, no, that's stupid. We need science. Science isn't bad by itself. It's just
bad when bad people use it to do bad things. We can do good things with
science. Like feed the world. I don't want to make all grown-ups slaves. My
parents are grown-ups, but they're all right.
Concerned Future Scientist
Louisiana 4:21 PM

Adide said . . .
I am afraid the grown-ups are going to destroy our planet. I want them to stop. I
wish they would use science to make better crops and make more rain. Instead
of bombs, they should make more schoolbooks for children.
Uganda 4:26 PM

Dita said . . .
I can't believe you and Max split up! You guys should stick together! Now I'm
even more worried about all of you! Be extra careful!
Mumbai 6:08 PM

Sean said . . .
Fang, I want to be a bird kid. I don't care what it takes. I would go through
anything to be able to fly and be with the flock. Tell me where to meet you. I
want to join you today.
Manchester, England 6:35 PM

YEAH, WE HAVE TO CROSS THE ATLANTIC OCEAN TO GET TO ENGLAND.

THERE'LL BE NO PLACE TO LAND AND REST FOR HOURS AND HOURS.

DO WE HAVE MONEY? ISN'T IT EXPENSIVE?

WELL...WE DON'T HAVE MONEY...

HMM?

...BUT WE DO HAVE A WAY...

YOU CAN GO NOW.

AH...YES... HAVE A PLEASANT FLIGHT...

THIS IS REALLY COMFORTABLE, BUT IT SEEMS WEIRD TO BE UP IN THE AIR AND NOT...

...OUTSIDE, YOU KNOW?

IT SEEMS KIND OF...UNNATURAL FOR A MACHINE TO BE, LIKE, UP IN THE AIR. I DON'T GET HOW IT'S STAYING UP.

IT'S GOT HONKING BIG ENGINES ON IT.

CLATTER

WE HAVE BEEFSTEAK AND CHICKEN PASTA TODAY. WHAT WOULD YOU LIKE?

AHH... HOW MUCH ARE THEY?

LONDON, HEATHROW AIRPORT

OKAY!

THE FIRST THING WE SHOULD DO IS FIND AN INTERNET CAFÉ, GET ON THE WEB...

...AND GOOGLE ITEX IN ENGLAND. EVEN IF WE DON'T FIND THEM BY NAME, WE'LL SEE OTHER LINKS THAT CAN HELP US.

WHOA, WHOA. ARE YOU TELLING ME... ...WE'RE NOT GOING TO GO SEE THE CROWN JEWELS?

Buckingham Palace!!

AND THE TOWER OF LONDON?

OOH, LOOK— MADAME TUSSAUDS! WE'VE GOT TO GO THERE!

ITEX PROBABLY HAS ITS MAIN OFFICES IN THE SUBURBS...

...NOT RIGHT IN THE CITY.

MAX...

...PLEASE?

WHOA.

THE IMPERIAL STATE CROWN. GOLLY. I WOULD LOVE TO HAVE A CROWN LIKE THAT.

THOSE AREN'T THE REAL JEWELS.

IT SAID THEY'RE REAL ON THE PLACARD.

......

WHAT DO YOU WANT TO EAT?

ARI?

TH-THIS?

HUH? BOTTLED WATER?

MENU

AH.

TURN

......

I-I'M THIRSTY.

ARI, YOU...

...YEAH...

I CAN'T READ.

JUST ORDER ANYTHING FOR ME.

THIS IS IT...

GEEZ, THEY'RE NOT EVEN PRETENDING TO GUSSY THIS PLACE UP, ARE THEY?

IT LOOKS SO DEPRESS-ING.

GRAB...

WHAT'S UP, ANGEL?

I CAN FEEL THOUGHTS AND STUFF COMING FROM INSIDE...

THEY'RE THINKING AWFUL STUFF.

61

GOT IT NOW, VOICE.

SMILE...

DOES ANYONE KNOW ANY FRENCH?

I KNOW SOME SPANISH.

TAP

CERRADO AND ABIERTO. STUFF LIKE THAT.

BUT WHY?

I BELIEVE FRANCE IS CALLING OUR NAMES.

FWOOOOSH

FRANCE?!

THIS WAY, DUDE.

CRASH HERE.

IT'S SAFE. AND OUR KIDS ARE ALWAYS ON GUARD AT THE FRONT DOOR.

THANK YOU SO MUCH!

NO PROB.

I WANT A GHOSTS JACKET.

......

......

HMPH.

HE DOESN'T EVEN ANSWER. I MISS MAX.

HAAH...

LET'S TAKE THE STAIRS.

WE'RE GOING TO THE TWENTY-SEVENTH FLOOR.

VRRRRRr

......

TING! 27

WRRR—

?

CAN I HELP YOU?

TMP

TMP

I NEED TO SPEAK TO YOUR TOP REPORTER.

I HAVE A STORY WITH WORLDWIDE IMPLICATIONS.

YOU PRINT WHAT I TELL YOU, AND THIS MAGAZINE WILL GO DOWN IN HISTORY.

......

I HADN'T THOUGHT OF IT. KEEZ IS RIGHT.

THAT WOULD HAVE WORKED LIKE A CHARM. SHOOT.

HUP!

THE PLAN IS HOT DOGS?

WE'RE JUST KILLING TIME TILL THE REAL PLAN FALLS INTO PLACE.

SHUDDER

......?!

WHAT?

YOU GUYS SCATTER!

WHAT'S GOING ON?

WE'VE GOT TROUBLE, BUT THEY'RE ONLY AFTER US!

HOW DO THEY KEEP FINDING US?

WE'LL STAY!

?

WHAT THE HECK IS THAT?!

ROBOTS.

YOU GUYS SHOULD SPLIT!

HOLY MOTHER...

WHOA, THEY DO HAVE WINGS!

EIGHTY FLYBOYS...

...COMING FROM TEN O'CLOCK.

ON THE GROUND, THE GHOSTS CAN HELP. LET'S TAKE THE AIR!

OKAY!

MAXIMUM
RIDE

MAXIMUM
RIDE
CHAPTER 37

LIFE IS SO SHORT...

THAT'S NOT SOMETHING A SIX-YEAR-OLD SHOULD SAY!

SO SHORT AND SO HARD. THE IDEA OF SEEING THE CITY OF LIGHT, JUST ONCE...

IT WOULD ALMOST MAKE EVERY-THING SEEM WORTHWHILE.

OH, FOR GOD'S SAKE.

PLEASE—

PLEASE—

OH, FINE! NOW GET OFF OF ME!

I can't fly!

YAAAY!!

IF I DIDN'T GIVE IN, THE VOICE WOULD HAVE POPPED UP WITH SOME SAGE ADVICE LIKE...

..."SEE WHAT PARIS HAS TO OFFER." OR, "WHAT'S THE LESSON YOU COULD LEARN FROM THIS?"

EUROPE WAS WEENSY. IT WAS LIKE, "OOPS, I BLINKED! THERE GOES BELGIUM!"

FLYING FROM ENGLAND TO FRANCE TOOK ABOUT THIRTY MINUTES. CROSSING OVER FRANCE TOOK ABOUT SIX HOURS. IT HAD TAKEN US ALMOST EIGHT HOURS TO CROSS TEXAS.

AND NOW WE WERE IN GERMANY.

THAT NIGHT.

HMM.

SEEMS EMPTY, AND I SEE COMPUTERS.

MAXIMUM
RIDE

MAXIMUM
RIDE
CHAPTER 38

I AM...

...YOUR MOTHER, MAX.

......

HOO, DELUSIONAL MUCH?

I KNOW IT'S HARD TO BELIEVE, BUT LOOK CLOSELY AT ME.

I'M AN OLDER VERSION OF YOU.

WELL, WELL, FANCY MEETING YOU.

ACTUALLY, NO ONE KNOWS I'M HERE.

COME HERE OFTEN? HOW'S THE FOOD?

SO YOU MET THE DIRECTOR?

YES. AND WHAT A PICNIC SHE TURNED OUT TO BE.

THREE BILLION WOMEN WITH OVARIES ON THIS PLANET, AND I HAD TO GET THE ONE VOTED "MOST LIKELY TO BECOME A DELUSIONAL PSYCHOPATH" AS MY MOM.

SSK..

TREMBLE TREMBLE

MAX...

URGENT! WE WANT OUR PLANET BACK!

Hey. If you get this message, we might have a chance. I mean the world might have a chance. Long story short: The grown-ups have taken a nice clean planet and trashed it for money. Not every grown-up. But a bunch of them, over and over, choose money and profits over clean air and water. It's their way of telling us they don't give a rat's butt about us, the kids, who are going to inherit what's left of the Earth.

A group of scientists want to take back the planet before it's too late and stop the pollution. Good, right? Only problem is they think they need to get rid of half the world's population to do it. So it's like: Save the planet so the pollution doesn't kill people, or . . . just kill people to start with, save everyone time. For you kids at home, that's called "flawed logic." I mean, call me crazy, but that seems like a really bad plan.

The other thing about these scientists is that they've tried to create a new kind of human who might survive better, like if there's a nuclear winter or whatever. I won't go into the details, but let me just say that this idea is as boneheaded and dangerous as their "Kill Half the People" plan.

What I'm saying is: It's up to us. You and me. Me and my flock, you and your friends. The kids. We want — we deserve — to inherit a clean, unmessed-up planet, and still keep everyone who's already living on it. We can do it. But we have to join together. We have to take chances. Take risks. We have to get active and really do something, instead of just sitting at home playing Xbox. This isn't a game. We can't defeat the enemy by hitting them with our superlaser guns.

We want our planet back.
Kids matter. We're important. Our future is important.
ARE YOU WITH ME?

GOSH.

IT'S LIKE LOOKING IN A MIRROR.

YEAH, EXCEPT I'VE HAD A BATH RECENTLY.

ANYWAY, WHAT ARE YOU DOING HERE?

SELLING GIRL SCOUT COOKIES. WANT SOME?

HOW CAN YOU JOKE AROUND?

THIS IS THE LAST STOP. THEY BROUGHT US HERE TO KILL US.

YEAH, I GET THAT A LOT.

......

149

PLEASE TELL ME THAT ICEBOX WAS KIDDING ABOUT BEING MY MOTHER.

THE DIRECTOR IS A BRILLIANT WOMAN...

...AN AMBITIOUS, TALENTED POLITICAL STRATEGIST.

SHE COULD VERY WELL END UP RUNNING THE WORLD.

AS HER DAUGHTER, YOU WOULD BE IN A POSITION OF UNIMAGINABLE ADVANTAGE.

EXCEPT THAT I WOULD HAVE CHANGED MY NAME AND DYED MY HAIR AND WOULD BE LIVING INCOGNITO TO AVOID THE EMBARRASSMENT OF HAVING A POWER-CRAZY DR. FRANKENSTEIN FOR A MOTHER!

IF I HAD THAT MUCH POWER, THE FIRST THING I WOULD DO IS SLAM HER INTO JAIL.

EVEN IF SHE WERE THE MOST POWERFUL PERSON IN THE WORLD AND GAVE YOU UNLIMITED POWER TOO?

PLUS ALL THE OTHERS WHO LENT A HAND TO THIS HATEFUL GOLD-FINGER PLAN OF WORLD DOMINATION.

WHAT DO YOU MEAN?

IS THIS ONE OF YOUR CHAIN YANKS? I MEAN, FOR GOD'S SAKE, MAKE UP YOUR MIND!

SHE ENGINEERED YOUR DESIGN AND DEVELOPMENT.

SHE OVERSAW THE WHOLE PROJECT. TO HER, THAT MUST FEEL LIKE MOTHERHOOD.

SHE DIDN'T DONATE AN EGG?

SHAKE
SHAKE

PHEW...

SHE SHARES NO GENETIC MATERIAL WITH YOU.

THANK GOD. I'M REALLY, REALLY GLAD.

......

YOU KILLED YOUR OWN BROTHER!

WELL? ANY OTHER BOMBS YOU WANT TO DROP?

DO YOU REMEMBER WHAT I SAID...

...WHEN YOU KILLED ARI IN NEW YORK?

SMIRK

HE *IS* YOUR BROTHER, MAX.

YEAH. LUCKY FOR YOU HE'S HARD TO KILL.

DR. MARTINEZ IS HISPANIC.

I DON'T LOOK ANYTHING LIKE HER.

IF THIS IS AN ELABORATE TEST, SOMETHING ELSE I'M SUPPOSED TO PASS SOMEHOW...

...YOU WILL NEVER SEE THE LIGHT OF DAY AGAIN.

YOU HAVE HER BROWN EYES.

THIS IS NOT A TEST. OUT OF EVERYTHING I'VE EVER TOLD YOU, THIS IS THE MOST TRUE.

VALENCIA MARTINEZ IS YOUR MOTHER. AND I'M YOUR FATHER.

I DON'T HAVE A FATHER.

SSK

MAX...

...YOU'RE STILL HERE TO SAVE THE WORLD. THAT'S WHAT YOU WERE BORN FOR...

...THAT'S THE POINT OF ALL OF THIS. NO ONE ELSE CAN DO IT. I BELIEVE THAT WITH ALL MY HEART.

......

WHAT ABOUT OUR PARENTS?

I DON'T KNOW. SOME OF THEM WERE NEVER IDENTIFIED BY NAME—ONLY NUMBER.

I DON'T KNOW WHAT YOU FOUND, BUT I'D GUESS YOU MISINTERPRETED THEM, OR MAYBE THEY WERE PLANTED BY THE DIRECTOR.

ME AND THE GASMAN. NUDGE, FANG. WHERE ARE THEY?

WHAT ABOUT THE NAMES AND ADDRESSES WE FOUND?

Fang's Blog

LET'S STICK TOGETHER, PEOPLE!

Okay, folks, we're on the East Coast somewhere between Miami and Eastport, Maine. Don't want to be more specific than that. We're on our way to rejoin Max. Don't have time to rehash all the details, but let's just say that I've decided a flock ought to stick together while they can.

We've gotten more mail than we can handle, so thanks to everyone who's supporting us. I can only reply to a few people, so I'll do that here, and then we have to split.

To Advon777 in Utah: I don't know where you got a missile launcher, and I don't want to know. But even though it might come in handy, it still seems like a really bad idea for you to be messing with it. Maybe you should just put it back where you got it.

To Felicite StarLight in Milan, Italy: Thanks for the offer, but I really don't have time for a girlfriend right now. I found your ideas . . . creative, but this is not a good time.

To JamesL in Ontario: Thanks, man. I appreciate your support. We need all the help we can get, but waiting till you get out of second grade is fine.

To PDM1223: Excellent! That's exactly what I'm talking about! Tell people what's going on, spread the message, organize protests and stuff. Picket the gargantuan pharmco companies like Itex. I hacked into their files and found that the companies Stellah Corp, Dywestra, Mofongo Research, DelaneyMinkerPrince, and a bunch of others are all Itex under different names in different countries. Stellah Corp is in England, not far from you.

See the whole list under Appendix F, for Fatheads.

Everyone, read this guy's mail! He totally has a handle on what I mean, what needs to happen.

To everyone in the Seattle area: There's a protest organized for Saturday. Check the schedule that BigBoyBlue has made (thanks, BBB!), attached as Appendix G, for the time and place. Folks in other cities, check the schedule. There's a tidal wave of stuff going on. Thanks to everyone who's making this happen!

We're gonna save the world! We're the last hope!

— Fang

WATCH OUT, GUYS, HERE WE COME

It's about five a.m. We should be sneaking on board the cargo plane soon. I've let the others sleep as much as they can — and of course now I'm so wiped I can't think straight. I'll try to grab some zzz's on the plane. Once it's up in the air, we're golden. We're probably the only people in the world who don't worry about plane crashes. If something happens to this plane and we start going down, I'll be like, later!
I hope Max is okay. Any of you guys — if you're around Lendeheim, Germany, go to the castle there and raise heck, okay?

— Fang

COLD...

THE RESULT OF MORE THAN SIX DECADES OF RESEARCH, HE IS AN UNQUALIFIED SUCCESS AND FAR SURPASSES ANY HYBRID MADE BEFORE.

IN ADDITION, HE HAS SUPERIOR MEMORY RETENTION AND REACTION TIME.

HE TESTS OFF THE CHARTS OF EVERY INTELLIGENCE SCALE DEVISED.

HE'S IMMUNE TO VIRTUALLY EVERY DISEASE KNOWN AND HAS SUPERACUTE REFLEXES AND GREATLY INCREASED STRENGTH.

HE'S TRULY A SUPERMAN!

PLUS, HE COOKS LIKE A DREAM AND MAKES DARLING FLORAL ARRANGEMENTS IN HIS SPARE TIME.

PFFT!

TO BEGIN, OMEGA WILL VANQUISH AN OBSOLETE BUT SOMEWHAT SUCCESSFUL HUMAN-AVIAN HYBRID.

MAX, ONE!

CHEATING DISQUALIFIES YOU!

I DIDN'T CHEAT! DID YOU SAY "NO FLYING"? DID ANYONE SAY "NO FLYING"?

NO.

IT WAS A RACE ON THE GROUND!

JUST BECAUSE WONDERLAD IS STUCK TO THE GROUND DOESN'T MEAN I HAVE TO BE.

YOU ARE DISQUALIFIED.

TSK

OMEGA IS THE WINNER.

YOU ARE A SCARY, SCARY CHILD, YOU KNOW THAT?

HEE-HEE!

THE BASE OF THEIR SPINES!

HIT THE FLYBOYS AT THE BASE OF THEIR SPINES!

JUMP

SLAM!

THUD

ARI!!

YOU HURT?

YOU GOT SHOT?!

MAX...

WHERE?

I... JUST...

OH, MAX...

To be continued in MAXIMUM RIDE, Vol. 7!

MAXIMUM RIDE: THE MANGA

BASED ON THE NOVELS BY
JAMES PATTERSON

ART AND ADAPTATION

NARAE LEE

BACKGROUND ASSISTANCE

WT.KIM

SPECIAL THANKS

MIMI . YOON

MAXIMUM RIDE: THE MANGA ⑥

JAMES PATTERSON
& NaRae Lee

Adaptation and Illustration: NaRae Lee

Lettering: JuYoun Lee

MAXIMUM RIDE, THE MANGA, Vol. 6 © 2012 by James Patterson

Illustrations © 2012 Hachette Book Group, Inc.

Yen Press
Hachette Book Group
237 Park Avenue, New York, NY 10017

HachetteBookGroup.com
YenPress.com

Yen Press is an imprint of Hachette Book Group, Inc. The Yen Press name and logo are trademarks of Hachette Book Group, Inc.

First Yen Press Edition: December 2012

ISBN: 978-0-7595-2972-4

10 9 8 7 6 5 4 3 2 1

BVG

Printed in the United States of America